Naomi Hefford
Illustrations by Lynsey Shaw

Counting All the Sheep

Bumblebee Books
London

BUMBLEBEE PAPERBACK EDITION

Copyright © Naomi Hefford 2022
Illustrations by Lynsey Shaw

A CIP catalogue record for this title is
available from the British Library.

ISBN: 978-1-83934-557-9

Bumblebee Books is an imprint of
Olympia Publishers.

First Published in 2022

Bumblebee Books
Tallis House
2 Tallis Street
London
EC4Y 0AB

Printed in Great Britain

www.olympiapublishers.com

Dedication

N.H
For Tillie and George.

L.S
For Dad
You would have loved reading this to Rebecca.

Out in the field with a baa and a meep

Were Mr Jacksons herd of sheep,

And just before bed

He counts every head

And his one hundred sheep go to sleep.

There's Molly and Milly and Danny and Mo

And Rupert and Hubert and Polly and Flo.

The family of Johnsons,

The Smiths and the Thompsons

And nine little lambs in a row.

There's Rita, Sunita, Jermaine and Jerome,

Morris, Doris, Elvis and his comb.

The Haydens and Laithwaits

And all of the Braithwaits

And Kevin with his garden gnome.

Then Harry and Sally and Billy and Ben

And weird cousin Stephen, who thinks he's a hen.

Sweet little Rosie

All sleepy and dozy,

But Lyla has run off again!

"That's not one hundred, no that's ninety-nine!"

Said old Mr Jackson, checking the time.

"I'll have to go look

In each cranny and nook

And I'll dig and I'll crawl and I'll climb."

So the field he left and the river he crossed.

"I must find my Lyla whatever the cost."

He left ninety-nine

In the evening sunshine.

"I must find the one that is lost."

He searched high and low and low and high,

He looked in the river and up to the sky.

He grazed his knees

Climbing trees,

He was so sad he started to cry.

baaaaaaaaaaaah

baaaaaaah

baaaaaaa

Then just in the distance, across the lake,

He thought he heard bleating, was this a mistake?

He ran to the sound

And that's where he found

Little Lyla eating meadow grass cake!

"Oh, Lyla," cried old Mr Jackson with glee,

"You're supposed to be back in the field with me!

Come let us go

To the others and throw

A huge great humongous party!"

So he put little Lyla over his shoulder

And set off for home, before it got colder.

They got to the field,

The Thompsons all squealed

And took it in turns to hold her.

So Molly and Milly and Danny and Mo

Danced all night through till almost tomorrow.

The Haydens and Laithwaits

Face painted the Braithwaits

And Rupert leapfrogged over Flo!

"I am so happy," Mr Jackson said,

"I left ninety-nine and went searching instead."

He hugged every one

Like a daughter or son

And counted them all.

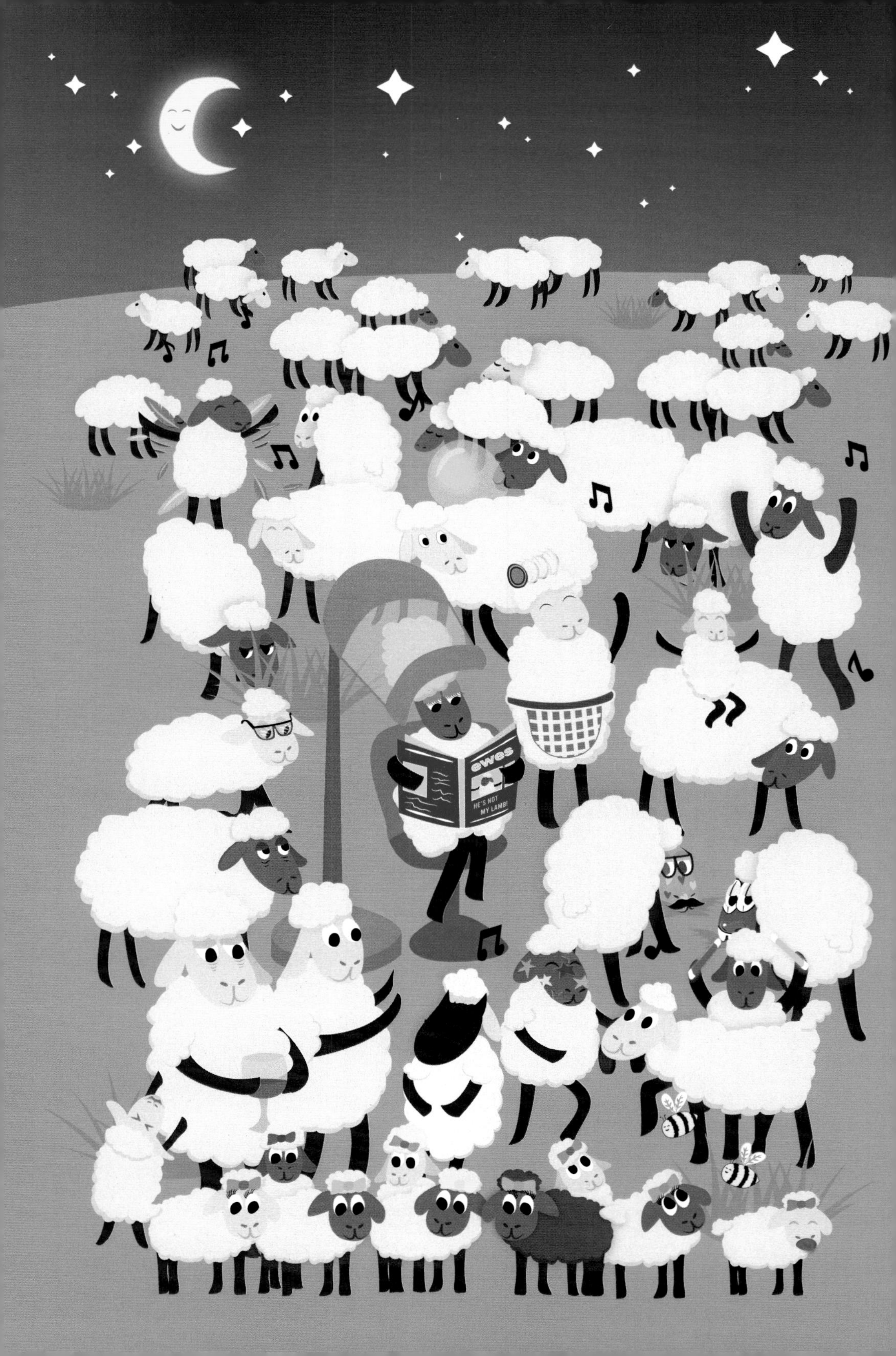
ewes
HE'S NOT MY LAMB!

100

About the Author

Naomi Hefford is a wife and mother and loves reading children's stories to her little ones. Naomi loves writing stories for children to enjoy, and bringing simple but important truths from the bible to life in colours and rhymes.

Acknowledgements

"What do you think? If a man owns a hundred sheep, and one of them wanders away, will he not leave the ninety-nine on the hills and go to look for the one that wandered off? And if he finds it, truly I tell you, he is happier about that one sheep than about the ninety-nine that did not wander off. In the same way your Father in heaven is not willing that any of these little ones should perish." Matthew 18:12-14